Andrew Brodie

G000253624

Improving
Spelling

for ages 9–10

A & C Black • London

Improving Spelling for Ages 9–10 features 42 sets of words, chosen to complement and extend the programme of activities that pupils will have experienced through 'Letters and Sounds'. The pupils will not need to work slavishly through the lists of words. However, if the lists are used on a regular basis as the focus for a short activity, they will help to provide a structured approach to improving pupils' skills in both reading and spelling.

Most pupils enjoy the security of following a repeated pattern in their work. Accordingly, each set of words is presented in two styles of sheet with which the pupils will soon become familiar:

SHEET A

SHEET B

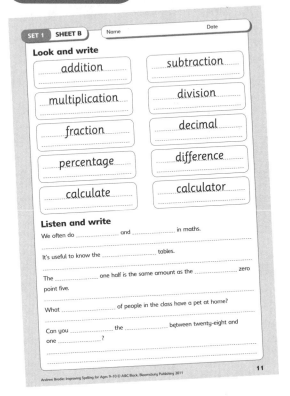

Sheet A features the 10 focus words to encourage the children to:

Look, listen and learn

This sheet can be:
- Displayed on the whiteboard for discussion.
- Copied on to card and cut up to make matching cards.
- Displayed on the wall as 'Words of the Week'.

Encouraging the children to 'sound-talk' the words. For example, the word pick can be sound-talked 'p-i-c-k' but be careful not to add 'uh' to sounds, i.e. say 'p' not 'puh'!

Sheet B provides practice activities:

Look and write

Encourages the children to look carefully at the structure of each word.

Listen and write

Encourages the children to listen carefully to the phonemes within each word, to help them to segment the word for spelling.

This sheet can be:
- Displayed on the whiteboard for discussion.
- Photocopied as individual activity sheets.
- Cut in half to make two separate activity sheets.

The book also features five sheets that can be copied and enlarged to make Spelling Strategy Posters, as recommended in 'Letters and Sounds'. You can use these as a focus for discussing strategies that pupils can employ when learning new spellings.

CONTENTS

PUPIL RECORD SHEET

You could record your pupils' progress using the 'traffic light' system: red for not yet secure, orange for secure, green for competent.

Name																								
Set 1																								
Set 2																								
Set 3																								
Set 4																								
Set 5																								
Set 6																								
Set 7																								
Set 8																								
Set 9																								
Set 10																								
Set 11																								
Set 12																								
Set 13																								
Set 14																								
Set 15																								
Set 16																								
Set 17																								
Set 18																								
Set 19																								
Set 20																								
Set 21																								
Set 22																								
Set 23																								
Set 24																								
Set 25																								
Set 26																								
Set 27																								
Set 28																								
Set 29																								
Set 30																								
Set 31																								
Set 32																								
Set 33																								
Set 34																								
Set 35																								
Set 36																								
Set 37																								
Set 38																								
Set 39																								
Set 40																								
Set 41																								
Set 42																								

To help me with spelling
I can use . . .

Syllables

by breaking words into chunks.

Look:

reflection

re-flec-tion

To help me with spelling
I can use . . .

Base words

Some words are based
on other words.

Look:

frightening

↓

The base word is **fright**.

To add the ing ending we need
to add the en.

Andrew Brodie: Improving Spelling for Ages 9–10 © A&C Black, Bloomsbury Publishing 2011

To help me with spelling
I can use . . .

Similar words

Some words are similar to other words.

Look:

musician

electrician

Both words have cian.

Andrew Brodie: Improving Spelling for Ages 9–10 © A&C Black, Bloomsbury Publishing 2011

To help me with spelling
I can use . . .

Mnemonics

If I'm really stuck I can make up a phrase or sentence to help me remember.

Look:

people

People **E**at **O**ther **P**eople's **L**unches **e**asily

If I am stuck on spelling a word I can . . .

1 use **phonics** to help me.

2 try breaking a big word into **syllables**.

3 think about whether it's made from a **base word**.

4 think about **similar words**.

5 **look** for the word.

6 **ask** for help.

7 use **mnemonics** to learn the word.

Look, listen and learn

addition	subtraction
multiplication	division
fraction	decimal
percentage	difference
calculate	calculator

Teacher's notes

Sheet A, Look, listen and learn: Use the words on this page as a focus for discussing phonic patterns and word structures. The pupils will notice that all of the words on this list are related to mathematics. Do they also notice that division ends differently to addition, subtraction and multiplication; that decimal, percentage and difference all feature a 'soft c'; and that subtraction, fraction, calculate and calculator all feature a 'hard c'? Ask pairs or small groups of children to create two spoken sentences using some of the words.

Sheet B, Look and write: Encourage the children to look closely at the words and to practise writing them.

Sheet B, Listen and write: Dictate each sentence below to the children, emphasising the target words and the revision word 'hundred'. Encourage the children to copy each sentence in full on the line underneath it. You could extend the activity by asking the children to make up their own sentence using one or more of the target words.

We often do addition and subtraction in maths.   It's useful to know the multiplication tables.
The fraction one half is the same amount as the decimal zero point five.
What percentage of people in the class have a pet at home?
Can you calculate the difference between twenty-eight and one hundred?

Look and write

addition	subtraction
multiplication	division
fraction	decimal
percentage	difference
calculate	calculator

Listen and write

We often do _____ and _____ in maths.

It's useful to know the _____ tables.

The _____ one half is the same amount as the _____ zero point five.

What _____ of people in the class have a pet at home?

Can you _____ the _____ between twenty-eight and one _____ ?

Look, listen and learn

calculation	multiply
divide	estimate
measure	approximate
approximation	question
questioning	answer

Teacher's notes

Sheet A, Look, listen and learn: Use the words on this page as a focus for discussing phonic patterns and word structures. The pupils will notice that all of the words on this list are concerned with mathematics and that some of the words are closely related. Ask pairs or small groups of children to create two spoken sentences using some of the words.

Sheet B, Look and write: Encourage the children to look closely at the words and to practise writing them.

Sheet B, Listen and write: Dictate each sentence below to the children, emphasising the target words and the word 'mathematics'. Encourage the children to copy each sentence in full on the line underneath it. You could extend the activity by asking the children to make up their own sentence using one or more of the target words.

Before you divide one number by another, make an estimate of the answer.
It's a good idea to make an approximation before any calculation.
When you multiply two numbers together the answer is often a large number.
Can you measure the length of the school field?   The teacher does a lot of questioning about mathematics!

Look and write

calculation

multiply

divide

estimate

measure

approximate

approximation

question

questioning

answer

Listen and write

Before you _____ one number by another, make an _____

of the _____.

_____

It's a good idea to make an _____ before any _____.

_____

When you _____ two numbers together the _____ is often

a large number.

_____

Can you _____ the length of the school field?

_____

The teacher does a lot of _____ about _____!

_____

Look, listen and learn

answering	measuring
double	doubling
half	halve
halving	quarter
quarters	third

Teacher's notes

Sheet A, Look, listen and learn: Use the words on this page as a focus for discussing phonic patterns and word structures. The pupils will notice that all of the words on this list are concerned with mathematics and that some of the words are closely related. Do they notice how the ending is altered when the singular word 'half' becomes plural or when it is used in its verb form? Ask pairs or small groups of children to create two spoken sentences using some of the words.

Sheet B, Look and write: Encourage the children to look closely at the words and to practise writing them.

Sheet B, Listen and write: Dictate each sentence below to the children, emphasising the target words. Encourage the children to copy each sentence in full on the line underneath it. You could extend the activity by asking the children to make up their own sentence using one or more of the target words.

Be careful when answering questions in mathematics.   Doubling a half of a number gets you back to the number itself! Halving the double of a number gets you back to that number.   Would you like a quarter of a cake or three quarters of a cake? Which is bigger, a third or a quarter?

Look and write

answering	measuring
double	doubling
half	halve
halving	quarter
quarters	third

Listen and write

Be careful when _____ questions in _____ .

_____ a _____ of a number gets you back to the number itself!

_____ the _____ of a number gets you back to that number.

Would you like a _____ of a cake or three _____ of a cake?

Which is bigger, a _____ or a _____ ?

Look, listen and learn

rectangle	square
triangle	circle
rhombus	hexagon
pentagon	parallel
parallelogram	measurement

Teacher's notes

Sheet A, Look, listen and learn: Use the words on this page as a focus for discussing phonic patterns and word structures. The pupils will notice that all of the words on this list are concerned with mathematics. Some of the words are apparently difficult to spell but by splitting them into their syllables or, even further, segmenting them into their phonemes they can become much easier. A useful extra clue in relation to the words 'parallel' and 'parallelogram' is to suggest that pupils consider the double 'l' in the word to be a pair of parallel lines. Ask pairs or small groups of children to create two spoken sentences using some of the words.

Sheet B, Look and write: Encourage the children to look closely at the words and to practise writing them.

Sheet B, Listen and write: Dictate each sentence below to the children, emphasising the target words and the word 'equal'. Encourage the children to copy each sentence in full on the line underneath it. You could extend the activity by asking the children to make up their own sentence using one or more of the target words.

A square is a type of rectangle with equal sides.   A triangle has three sides but a circle has only one side.
A rhombus has four equal sides but its corners are not equal.   The opposite sides of a rectangle are parallel.
The sides of a square are equal in measurement.

Andrew Brodie: Improving Spelling for Ages 9–10 © A&C Black, Bloomsbury Publishing 2011

Look and write

rectangle	square
triangle	circle
rhombus	hexagon
pentagon	parallel
parallelogram	measurement

Listen and write

A _____ is a type of _____ with _____ sides.

A _____ has three sides but a _____ has only one side.

A _____ has four _____ sides but its corners are not

_____.

The opposite sides of a _____ are _____.

The sides of a _____ are _____ in _____.

Look, listen and learn

positive	negative
weather	temperature
zero	minus
decade	century
year	millennium

Teacher's notes

Sheet A, Look, listen and learn: Use the words on this page as a focus for discussing phonic patterns and word structures. Again, many of these words are used in relation to mathematics. Breaking the words into their syllables and discussing features of each syllable in relation to their letters and sounds can make them easier to spell and remember. Ask pairs or small groups of children to create two spoken sentences using some of the words.

Sheet B, Look and write: Encourage the children to look closely at the words and to practise writing them.

Sheet B, Listen and write: Dictate each sentence below to the children, emphasising the target words. Encourage the children to copy each sentence in full on the line underneath it. You could extend the activity by asking the children to make up their own sentence using one or more of the target words.

In summer the temperature is shown by the positive numbers on a thermometer.
In winter the temperature is sometimes shown by the negative numbers on a thermometer.
On the 26th January the temperature was minus seven degrees Celsius.
On the 27th January the temperature was slightly above zero.   There are ten decades in each century.

Look and write

positive	negative
weather	temperature
zero	minus
decade	century
year	millennium

Listen and write

In summer the _____ is shown by the _____ numbers on a thermometer.

_____

In winter the _____ is sometimes shown by the _____ numbers on a thermometer.

_____

_____

On the 26th January the _____ was _____ seven degrees Celsius.

_____

On the 27th January the _____ was slightly above _____.

_____

There are ten _____ in each _____.

_____

Look, listen and learn

area	perimeter
circumference	centre
radius	diameter
balance	weigh
weight	scales

Teacher's notes

Sheet A, Look, listen and learn: Use the words on this page as a focus for discussing phonic patterns and word structures. Again, many of these words are used in relation to mathematics. Breaking the words into their syllables and discussing features of each syllable in relation to their letters and sounds can make them easier to spell and remember. Encourage the children to look closely at the spelling of the phoneme /ai/ in the words 'weigh' and 'weight'. Ask pairs or small groups of children to create two spoken sentences using some of the words.

Sheet B, Look and write: Encourage the children to look closely at the words and to practise writing them.

Sheet B, Listen and write: Dictate each sentence below to the children, emphasising the target words. Encourage the children to copy each sentence in full on the line underneath it. You could extend the activity by asking the children to make up their own sentence using one or more of the target words.

The perimeter of a shape is the distance measured around it.   The perimeter of a circle is called its circumference.
A radius is a straight line from the centre of a circle to its circumference.
A diameter is a straight line passing through the centre of a circle and touching the circumference at each end.
We can find the weight of an object by using scales.

Look and write

area	perimeter
circumference	centre
radius	diameter
balance	weigh
weight	scales

Listen and write

The _____ of a shape is the distance _____ around it.

The _____ of a circle is called its _____.

A _____ is a straight line from the _____ of a circle to its

_____.

A _____ is a straight line passing through the _____ of a

circle and touching the _____ at each end.

We can find the _____ of an object by using _____.

Look, listen and learn

cube	cuboid
pyramid	sphere
cone	cylinder
prism	tetrahedron
circumnavigate	circumstances

Teacher's notes

Sheet A, Look, listen and learn: Use the words on this page as a focus for discussing phonic patterns and word structures. What do all the words have in common? Most are related to maths but the final two share the same prefix as the word 'circumference' and provide revision of this prefix. Ask pairs or small groups of children to create two spoken sentences using some of the words.

Sheet B, Look and write: Encourage the children to look closely at the words and to practise writing them.

Sheet B, Listen and write: Dictate each sentence below to the children, emphasising the target words and the revision words, 'measured', 'measuring' and 'world'. Encourage the children to copy each sentence in full on the line underneath it. You could extend the activity by asking the children to make up their own sentence using one or more of the target words.

A cube and a cuboid each have six faces.   A tetrahedron is a triangular pyramid.
We measured an amount of water by using a measuring cylinder.   Our world is a sphere.
I would like to circumnavigate the world.

Look and write

cube	cuboid
pyramid	sphere
cone	cylinder
prism	tetrahedron
circumnavigate	circumstances

Listen and write

A _____ and a _____ each have six faces.

_____

A _____ is a triangular _____.

_____

We _____ an amount of water by using a _____

_____.

_____

_____

Our _____ is a _____.

_____

I would like to _____ the _____.

_____

Look, listen and learn

symmetry	symmetrical
reflect	reflection
angle	acute
obtuse	horizontal
vertical	diagonal

Teacher's notes

Sheet A, Look, listen and learn: Use the words on this page as a focus for discussing phonic patterns and word structures. Ensure that the children understand the meaning of each word. Ask pairs or small groups of children to create two spoken sentences using some of the words – can they make up some sentences that are related to maths but others that are related to non-mathematical ideas?

Sheet B, Look and write: Encourage the children to look closely at the words and to practise writing them.

Sheet B, Listen and write: Dictate each sentence below to the children, emphasising the target words and the revision words. Encourage the children to copy each sentence in full on the line underneath it. You could extend the activity by asking the children to make up their own sentence using one or more of the target words.

Some houses are built in a symmetrical style.   Sometimes my reflection gives me a shock!
An acute angle is less than ninety degrees.
An obtuse angle is greater than ninety degrees but smaller than one hundred and eighty degrees.
Most floors are horizontal and most walls are vertical.

Look and write

symmetry	symmetrical
reflect	reflection
angle	acute
obtuse	horizontal
vertical	diagonal

Listen and write

Some houses are built in a _____ style.

_____

_____ my _____ gives me a shock!

_____

An _____ angle is less than _____ degrees.

_____

An _____ angle is greater than _____ degrees but

smaller than one hundred and _____ degrees.

_____

Most floors are _____ and most walls are _____.

_____

Look, listen and learn

verb	adverb
adjective	noun
pronoun	punctuation
metaphor	dialogue
speech	script

Teacher's notes

Sheet A, Look, listen and learn: Use the words on this page as a focus for discussing phonic patterns and word structures. Encourage the pupils to notice that the words are all related to their work in literacy lessons. Ask pairs or small groups of children to create two spoken sentences using some of the words.

Sheet B, Look and write: Encourage the children to look closely at the words and to practise writing them.

Sheet B, Listen and write: Dictate each sentence below to the children, emphasising the target words and revision words such as 'something' and 'important'. Encourage the children to copy each sentence in full on the line underneath it. You could extend the activity by asking the children to make up their own sentence using one or more of the target words.

An adverb is often used with a verb to show how something was done.
An adjective is often used as a descriptive word with a noun.
A pronoun can sometimes be used in place of a noun.   It is important to use punctuation correctly.
A play script may contain important speeches.

Look and write

verb

adverb

adjective

noun

pronoun

punctuation

metaphor

dialogue

speech

script

Listen and write

An _____ is often used with a _____ to show how

_____ was done.

_____

_____

An _____ is often used as a descriptive word with a _____.

_____

A _____ can sometimes be used in place of a _____.

_____

It is _____ to use _____ correctly.

_____

A play _____ may contain _____ _____.

_____

Look, listen and learn

homophone	rode
rowed	road
beach	beech
witch	which
weather	whether

Teacher's notes

Sheet A, Look, listen and learn: Use the words on this page as a focus for discussing phonic patterns and word structures. Point out that all of the words, apart from homophone itself, are homophones, ie each word sounds like another of different meaning. Ask pairs or small groups of children to create two spoken sentences using some of the words.

Sheet B, Look and write: Encourage the children to look closely at the words and to practise writing them.

Sheet B, Listen and write: Dictate each sentence below to the children, emphasising the target words and the revision words. Encourage the children to copy each sentence in full on the line underneath it. Can the children apply their knowledge of how to add 'ly' to base words when they have to spell words such as 'carefully'? You could extend the activity by asking the children to make up their own sentence using one or more of the target words.

I rode my bike carefully along the road.
I rowed the boat to the middle of the lake then the weather changed and I got soaked by the rain.
There are not many beech trees near the beach.   I didn't know which way to go.
I didn't know whether to turn left or right.

Look and write

homophone	rode
rowed	road
beach	beech
witch	which
weather	whether

Listen and write

I _____ my bike _____ along the _____.

_____

I _____ the boat to the _____ of the lake then the _____ changed and I got _____ by the rain.

_____

_____

There are not many _____ trees near the _____.

_____

I didn't know _____ way to go.

_____

I didn't know _____ to turn left or right.

_____

Look, listen and learn

nice	twice
police	notice
niece	scene
scale	accident
accidental	accidentally

Teacher's notes

Sheet A, Look, listen and learn: Use the words on this page as a focus for discussing phonic patterns and word structures. Ask the children to compare the sound made by each letter 'c' – do they notice that sometimes the letter c represents the phoneme /k/ and sometimes the phoneme /s/? In the word accident the first 'c' represents /k/ and the second represents /s/. Ask pairs or small groups of children to create two spoken sentences using some of the words.

Sheet B, Look and write: Encourage the children to look closely at the words and to practise writing them.

Sheet B, Listen and write: Dictate each sentence below to the children, emphasising the target words. Encourage the children to copy each sentence in full on the line underneath it. You could extend the activity by asking the children to make up their own sentence using one or more of the target words.

I think ice-cream is twice as nice as jelly!   The police put up a notice about the accident.
The young couple took their niece and nephew on holiday.   She fell over accidentally in the first scene of the play.
Nobody noticed the scale of the flood at first.

Look and write

nice

twice

police

notice

niece

scene

scale

accident

accidental

accidentally

Listen and write

I think ice-cream is _____ as _____ as jelly!

The _____ put up a _____ about the _____.

The young couple took their _____ and nephew on _____.

She fell over _____ in the first _____ of the play.

Nobody _____ the _____ of the flood at first.

Look, listen and learn

piano	pianos
tomato	tomatoes
potato	potatoes
echo	echoes
volcano	volcanoes

Teacher's notes

Sheet A, Look, listen and learn: Use the words on this page as a focus for discussing phonic patterns and word structures. Each of the singular words ends with the letter 'o' – can the pupils point out which plural is the 'odd one out'? Ask pairs or small groups of children to create two spoken sentences using some of the words.

Sheet B, Look and write: Encourage the children to look closely at the words and to practise writing them.

Sheet B, Listen and write: Dictate each sentence below to the children, emphasising the target words and the revision words. Encourage the children to copy each sentence in full on the line underneath it. You could extend the activity by asking the children to make up their own sentence using one or more of the target words.

I wish I could play the piano.   There are two pianos in the school.
Tomato sauce is made from tomatoes but also contains vinegar, sugar and salt.   Crisps are made from potatoes.
There are no active volcanoes in this country.

Look and write

piano	pianos
tomato	tomatoes
potato	potatoes
echo	echoes
volcano	volcanoes

Listen and write

I wish I _____ play the _____.

There are two _____ in the _____.

_____ sauce is made from _____ but also _____ vinegar, sugar and salt.

_____ are made from _____.

There are no active _____ in this _____.

Look, listen and learn

kangaroo	tattoo
igloo	cuckoo
shampoo	banana
camera	umbrella
bacteria	sofa

Teacher's notes

Sheet A, Look, listen and learn: Use the words on this page as a focus for discussing phonic patterns and word structures. All of these words feature final vowels – can the children think of any words that end with the vowel 'i' or the vowel 'u'? Ask pairs or small groups of children to create two spoken sentences using some of the words.

Sheet B, Look and write: Encourage the children to look closely at the words and to practise writing them.

Sheet B, Listen and write: Dictate each sentence below to the children, emphasising the target words and the revision words. Show the children the spelling of the word 'cause' before they start the sentences. Point out the use of the apostrophe after the word birds' (showing ownership by more than one bird). Encourage the children to copy each sentence in full on the line underneath it. You could extend the activity by asking the children to make up their own sentence using one or more of the target words.

I saw a grey kangaroo and a red kangaroo.   An igloo is a house made of blocks of snow.
The cuckoo lays its eggs in other birds' nests.   Put the umbrella up to keep the camera dry.
Some bacteria can cause diseases.

     Andrew Brodie: Improving Spelling for Ages 9–10 © A&C Black, Bloomsbury Publishing 2011

Look and write

kangaroo	tattoo
igloo	cuckoo
shampoo	banana
camera	umbrella
bacteria	sofa

Listen and write

I saw a grey _____ and a red _____ .

An _____ is a house made of _____ of snow.

The _____ lays its eggs in other birds' nests.

Put the _____ up to keep the _____ dry.

Some _____ can _____ diseases.

Look, listen and learn

active	captive
forgive	massive
expensive	alive
arrive	drive
arrival	actively

Teacher's notes

Sheet A, Look, listen and learn: Use the words on this page as a focus for discussing phonic patterns and word structures. All of these words feature the ending 'ive' or are derived from such words. Ask pairs or small groups of children to create two spoken sentences using some of the words.

Sheet B, Look and write: Encourage the children to look closely at the words and to practise writing them.

Sheet B, Listen and write: Dictate each sentence below to the children, emphasising the target words and the revision words. Show the children the word 'announced' before dictating the sentences. Encourage the children to copy each sentence in full on the line underneath it. You could extend the activity by asking the children to make up their own sentence using one or more of the target words.

It is important to have active lifestyles.   We should forgive people who make mistakes.
A massive volcano erupted in Iceland.   The arrival of the train was announced.
It is costly to drive a car because petrol is so expensive.

Name

Date

Look and write

active	captive
forgive	massive
expensive	alive
arrive	drive
arrival	actively

Listen and write

It is _____ to have _____ lifestyles.

We should _____ people who make _____.

A _____ _____ erupted in Iceland.

The _____ of the train was _____.

It is costly to _____ a car because petrol is so _____.

Look, listen and learn

library	February
jewellery	Wednesday
generally	miserable
business	factory
dictionary	separate

Teacher's notes

Sheet A, Look, listen and learn: Use the words on this page as a focus for discussing phonic patterns and word structures. All of these words contain unsounded elements – can the children identify the unsounded part of each word? Ask pairs or small groups of children to create two spoken sentences using some of the words.

Sheet B, Look and write: Encourage the children to look closely at the words and to practise writing them.

Sheet B, Listen and write: Dictate each sentence below to the children, emphasising the target words. Encourage the children to copy each sentence in full on the line underneath it. You could extend the activity by asking the children to make up their own sentence using one or more of the target words.

There are lots of books in the library.   My dental appointment is on Wednesday the 8th of February.
It's generally better to be happy than miserable.   The successful business has a very large factory.
Look up the word separate in the dictionary.

        Andrew Brodie: Improving Spelling for Ages 9–10 © A&C Black, Bloomsbury Publishing 2011

Name   Date

Look and write

library   February

jewellery   Wednesday

generally   miserable

business   factory

dictionary   separate

Listen and write

There are lots of books in the _____.

My dental appointment is on _____ the 8th of _____.

It's _____ better to be happy than _____.

The successful _____ has a very large _____.

Look up the word _____ in the _____.

Look, listen and learn

water	liquid
solid	evaporate
evaporation	oxygen
carbon dioxide	vapour
freezing	frozen

Teacher's notes

Sheet A, Look, listen and learn: Use the words on this page as a focus for discussing phonic patterns and word structures. Do the children notice that all of these words may appear in their science work? Ask pairs or small groups of children to create two spoken sentences using some of the words.

Sheet B, Look and write: Encourage the children to look closely at the words and to practise writing them.

Sheet B, Listen and write: Dictate each sentence below to the children, emphasising the target words and the word 'slippery'. Encourage the children to copy each sentence in full on the line underneath it. You could extend the activity by asking the children to make up their own sentence using one or more of the target words.

When water freezes it becomes ice.   Ice is a solid, not a liquid.
When water evaporates it becomes vapour.   We breathe in oxygen and breathe out carbon dioxide.
The frozen puddle was very slippery.

Look and write

water	liquid
solid	evaporate
evaporation	oxygen
carbon dioxide	vapour
freezing	frozen

Listen and write

When _____ _____ it becomes ice.

_____

Ice is a _____, not a _____.

_____

When _____ _____ it becomes _____.

_____

We breathe in _____ and breathe out _____.

_____

The _____ puddle was very _____.

_____

Look, listen and learn

heart	pulse
blood	lungs
muscles	body
brain	liver
kidney	stomach

Teacher's notes

Sheet A, Look, listen and learn: Use the words on this page as a focus for discussing phonic patterns and word structures. The children will notice that all of these words represent parts of the body. Ask pairs or small groups of children to create two spoken sentences using some of the words.

Sheet B, Look and write: Encourage the children to look closely at the words and to practise writing them.

Sheet B, Listen and write: Dictate each sentence below to the children, emphasising the target words. Encourage the children to copy each sentence in full on the line underneath it. You could extend the activity by asking the children to make up their own sentence using one or more of the target words.

The heart and lungs are in the chest.   The heart pumps blood around the body.
All our thoughts happen in our brains.   The liver and the kidneys are important organs of the body.
The digestion of food starts in the stomach.

    Andrew Brodie: Improving Spelling for Ages 9–10 © A&C Black, Bloomsbury Publishing 2011

Look and write

heart	pulse
blood	lungs
muscles	body
brain	liver
kidney	stomach

Listen and write

The _____ and _____ are in the _____.

_____

The _____ pumps _____ around the _____.

_____

All our thoughts happen in our _____.

_____

The _____ and the _____ are important organs of the

_____.

_____

The digestion of food starts in the _____.

_____

Look, listen and learn

flower	female
carpel	stigma
style	ovary
male	stamen
anther	filament

Sheet A, Look, listen and learn: Use the words on this page as a focus for discussing phonic patterns and word structures. These words will be of use to the children when studying parts of a flower. Ask pairs or small groups of children to create two spoken sentences using some of the words.

Sheet B, Look and write: Encourage the children to look closely at the words and to practise writing them.

Sheet B, Listen and write: Dictate each sentence below to the children, emphasising the target words. Encourage the children to copy each sentence in full on the line underneath it. You could extend the activity by asking the children to make up their own sentence using one or more of the target words.

Flowers have male and female parts.   The carpel is the female part.
The stamen is the male part.   The stigma, style and ovary are all parts of the carpel.
The anther and filament are parts of the stamen.

Name

Date

Look and write

flower	female
carpel	stigma
style	ovary
male	stamen
anther	filament

Listen and write

_____ have _____ and _____ parts.

The _____ is the _____ part.

The _____ is the _____ part.

The _____, _____ and _____ are all parts of

the _____ .

The _____ and _____ are parts of the _____ .

Look, listen and learn

music	musical
musician	orchestra
choir	conductor
instrument	instrumental
percussion	woodwind

Teacher's notes

Sheet A, Look, listen and learn: Use the words on this page as a focus for discussing phonic patterns and word structures. All of these words are related to music and all can give excellent practice of the processes of syllabification and segmentation. Point out the 'cian' ending of 'musician' and the grapheme 'ch' representing the phoneme /k/ in the word 'orchestra'. Ask pairs or small groups of children to create two spoken sentences using some of the words.

Sheet B, Look and write: Encourage the children to look closely at the words and to practise writing them.

Sheet B, Listen and write: Dictate each sentence below to the children, emphasising the target words. Encourage the children to copy each sentence in full on the line underneath it. You could extend the activity by asking the children to make up their own sentence using one or more of the target words.

There are lots of musicians in an orchestra.   The conductor is in charge of the orchestra.
I would like to play a musical instrument.   Drums and cymbals are percussion instruments.
Clarinets and oboes are woodwind instruments.

     Andrew Brodie: Improving Spelling for Ages 9–10 © A&C Black, Bloomsbury Publishing 2011

Look and write

music	musical
musician	orchestra
choir	conductor
instrument	instrumental
percussion	woodwind

Listen and write

There are lots of _____ in an _____.

The _____ is in charge of the _____.

I would like to play a _____ _____.

Drums and cymbals are _____ _____.

Clarinets and oboes are _____ _____.

Look, listen and learn

history	geography
religion	religious
education	physical
technology	English
literacy	mathematics

Sheet A, Look, listen and learn: Use the words on this page as a focus for discussing phonic patterns and word structures. The spelling of the names of school subjects again provides practice of syllabification and segmentation – do the children notice the grapheme 'ph' representing /f/ and the grapheme 'ch' representing /k/? Ask pairs or small groups of children to create two spoken sentences using some of the words.

Sheet B, Look and write: Encourage the children to look closely at the words and to practise writing them.

Sheet B, Listen and write: Dictate each sentence below to the children, emphasising the target words and the word 'information'. Encourage the children to copy each sentence in full on the line underneath it. You could extend the activity by asking the children to make up their own sentence using one or more of the target words.

This afternoon we are learning about history and geography.   We learn about different religions in religious education.
The abbreviation of physical education is PE.   We use computers for information technology.
We usually work on literacy and mathematics in the morning.

Look and write

history	geography
religion	religious
education	physical
technology	English
literacy	mathematics

Listen and write

This afternoon we are learning about _____ and _____.

_____

We learn about different _____ in _____

_____.

_____

_____

The abbreviation of _____ _____ is PE.

_____

We use computers for _____ _____.

_____

We usually work on _____ and _____ in the morning.

_____

Look, listen and learn

kiwi	bhaji
ski	spaghetti
fungi	ravioli
macaroni	alibi
chapatti	confetti

Teacher's notes

Sheet A, Look, listen and learn: Use the words on this page as a focus for discussing phonic patterns and word structures. Do the pupils notice that all of the words end with the vowel 'i'? Most of the words concern food – can the pupils identify those that do not? Ask them to add the endings 'ing' and 'ed' to the word 'ski'. Ask pairs or small groups of children to create two spoken sentences using some of the words.

Sheet B, Look and write: Encourage the children to look closely at the words and to practise writing them.

Sheet B, Listen and write: Dictate each sentence below to the children, emphasising the target words and the revision words. Encourage the children to copy each sentence in full on the line underneath it. You could extend the activity by asking the children to make up their own sentence using one or more of the target words.

A kiwi fruit is bright green but has a brown skin.   Macaroni and spaghetti are both types of pasta.
Chapatti and bhaji are both Indian foods.   Toadstools and mushrooms are types of fungi.
Lots of confetti was thrown over the bride and groom.

Look and write

kiwi

bhaji

ski

spaghetti

fungi

ravioli

macaroni

alibi

chapatti

confetti

Listen and write

A _____ fruit is _____ green but has a brown skin.

_____ and _____ are both types of pasta.

_____ and _____ are both Indian foods.

Toadstools and mushrooms are types of _____.

Lots of _____ was _____ over the _____

and _____.

Look, listen and learn

party	parties
city	cities
body	bodies
carry	carries
copy	copies

Teacher's notes

Sheet A, Look, listen and learn: Use the words on this page as a focus for discussing phonic patterns and word structures. Do the pupils notice that the words are arranged in pairs? Which pair is different to the others? (Carry and carries are not nouns, copy and copies could be nouns or verbs depending on usage.) Ask pairs or small groups of children to create two spoken sentences using some of the words.

Sheet B, Look and write: Encourage the children to look closely at the words and to practise writing them.

Sheet B, Listen and write: Dictate each sentence below to the children, emphasising the target words and the revision words including the word 'don't', which features an apostrophe for the omission of the letter 'o'. Encourage the children to copy each sentence in full on the line underneath it. You could extend the activity by asking the children to make up their own sentence using one or more of the target words.

Do people in cities have lots of parties?   Our blood carries oxygen around our bodies.
The teacher made lots of copies of the play script.   I had to carry the box of books across the busiest road in the city.
Copy the words carefully so that you don't make any mistakes.

Name   Date

Look and write

party	parties
city	cities
body	bodies
carry	carries
copy	copies

Listen and write

Do people in _____ have lots of _____?

_____

Our _____ _____ _____ around our _____.

_____

The teacher made lots of _____ of the play _____.

_____

I had to _____ the box of books across the busiest road in the _____.

_____

_____ the words _____ so that you _____ make any mistakes.

_____

_____

Look, listen and learn

railway	monorail
airport	airfield
waterside	dockyard
boatyard	aeroplane
shipbuilding	airways

Teacher's notes

Sheet A, Look, listen and learn: Use the words on this page as a focus for discussing phonic patterns and word structures. The words are related to travel and many of them are compound words. Ask pairs or small groups of children to create two spoken sentences using some of the words.

Sheet B, Look and write: Encourage the children to look closely at the words and to practise writing them.

Sheet B, Listen and write: Dictate each sentence below to the children, emphasising the target words and the revision word 'girl's', which features an apostrophe for ownership. Encourage the children to copy each sentence in full on the line underneath it. You could extend the activity by asking the children to make up their own sentence using one or more of the target words.

The small aeroplane landed on the grass at the airfield.   Hundreds of aeroplanes land at Heathrow airport every day.
Boatbuilding takes place in a boatyard and shipbuilding takes place in a shipyard.
Ships can be built or repaired in a dockyard.   The monorail links the two main railway stations.

Look and write

railway	monorail
airport	airfield
waterside	dockyard
boatyard	aeroplane
shipbuilding	airways

Listen and write

The small _____ landed on the grass at the _____ .

Hundreds of _____ land at Heathrow _____ every day.

_____ takes place in a _____ and _____

takes place in a _____ .

Ships can be _____ or repaired in a _____ .

The _____ links the two main _____ stations.

Andrew Brodie: Improving Spelling for Ages 9–10 © A&C Black, Bloomsbury Publishing 2011

Look, listen and learn

wolf	wolves
knife	knives
myself	himself
herself	themselves
selfish	selfishness

Teacher's notes

Sheet A, Look, listen and learn: Use the words on this page as a focus for discussing phonic patterns and word structures. What do the pupils notice about the set of words? There are two main patterns to be observed: the ves ending for the plurals of some words that end with 'f' and the set of words linked to the base word 'self'. Ask pairs or small groups of children to create two spoken sentences using some of the words.

Sheet B, Look and write: Encourage the children to look closely at the words and to practise writing them.

Sheet B, Listen and write: Dictate each sentence below to the children, emphasising the target words and the revision words. You may wish to focus on the word believed. Encourage the children to copy each sentence in full on the line underneath it. You could extend the activity by asking the children to make up their own sentence using one or more of the target words.

The boy kept shouting 'wolf' so the people came running to help him look after the sheep but there were never any wolves there.
Each time the boy shouted 'wolf', the people armed themselves with knives.
When the wolves really came nobody believed the boy when he shouted.
Because of the boy's selfishness all the sheep were killed by the wolves.

    Andrew Brodie: Improving Spelling for Ages 9–10 © A&C Black, Bloomsbury Publishing 2011

Look and write

wolf	wolves
knife	knives
myself	himself
herself	themselves
selfish	selfishness

Listen and write

The boy kept shouting '_____' so the _____ came running to help him look after the sheep but there were never any _____ there.

_____

_____

Each time the boy shouted '_____', the _____ armed _____ with _____.

_____

_____

When the _____ really came nobody _____ the boy when he shouted.

_____

Because of the boy's _____ all the sheep were killed by the _____.

_____

Look, listen and learn

teeth	children
people	women
fungi	fish
sheep	geese
mice	hobbies

Teacher's notes

Sheet A, Look, listen and learn: Use the words on this page as a focus for discussing phonic patterns and word structures. All of the words on this list are plurals and a worthwhile extra activity would be to ask the pupils to find the singular for each one. Some of the words have been practised before but are often found to be quite challenging. Ask pairs or small groups of children to create two spoken sentences using some of the words.

Sheet B, Look and write: Encourage the children to look closely at the words and to practise writing them.

Sheet B, Listen and write: Dictate each sentence below to the children, emphasising the target words and the revision words. Encourage the children to copy each sentence in full on the line underneath it. You could extend the activity by asking the children to make up their own sentence using one or more of the target words.

When the Titanic sank, the women and children were the first people sent to the lifeboats.
Some fungi are dangerous to eat.   The dentist helps us to look after our teeth.
I woke early this morning because the sheep and the geese were making so much noise.   Do you think mice have hobbies?

Name   Date

Look and write

_____ teeth _____

_____ children _____

_____ people _____

_____ women _____

_____ fungi _____

_____ fish _____

_____ sheep _____

_____ geese _____

_____ mice _____

_____ hobbies _____

Listen and write

When the Titanic sank, the _____ and _____ were the

first _____ sent to the lifeboats.

_____

_____

Some _____ are dangerous to eat.

_____

The _____ helps us to look after our _____.

_____

I woke _____ this morning because the _____ and the

_____ were making so much noise.

_____

_____

Do you think _____ have _____?

_____

Look, listen and learn

automobile	autobiography
autograph	telephone
television	telescope
transport	transparent
transatlantic	transform

Teacher's notes

Sheet A, Look, listen and learn: Use the words on this page as a focus for discussing phonic patterns and word structures. Do the children notice that the words either start with the prefix 'auto' or 'trans'? They may be interested to know that 'auto' is derived from Greek, meaning self and that 'trans' is derived from Latin, meaning across. Ask pairs or small groups of children to create two spoken sentences using some of the words.

Sheet B, Look and write: Encourage the children to look closely at the words and to practise writing them.

Sheet B, Listen and write: Dictate each sentence below to the children, emphasising the target words and the revision words. Encourage the children to copy each sentence in full on the line underneath it. You could extend the activity by asking the children to make up their own sentence using one or more of the target words.

After she wrote her autobiography, lots of people asked for her autograph.   The automobile is a very common form of transport. I was watching television when the telephone rang.   The first transatlantic flight transformed world travel. Most windows have transparent glass.

Name   Date

Look and write

automobile	autobiography
autograph	telephone
television	telescope
transport	transparent
transatlantic	transform

Listen and write

After she wrote her _____, lots of people asked for her

_____.

_____

_____

The _____ is a very common form of _____.

_____

I was watching _____ when the _____ rang.

_____

The first _____ flight _____ world _____.

_____

Most windows have _____ glass.

_____

Look, listen and learn

binoculars	biceps
bicentenary	monorail
unicycle	monosyllable
bicycle	triangle
triangular	tricycle

Teacher's notes

Sheet A, Look, listen and learn: Use the words on this page as a focus for discussing phonic patterns and word structures. The children may be interested to know that the prefix 'mono' is derived from the Greek for alone, 'bi' is from Latin and 'tri' is from Greek. They may also be aware of the prefix 'uni', derived from the Latin for one. Ask pairs or small groups of children to create two spoken sentences using some of the words.

Sheet B, Look and write: Encourage the children to look closely at the words and to practise writing them.

Sheet B, Listen and write: Dictate each sentence below to the children, emphasising the target words and the revision words. Encourage the children to copy each sentence in full on the line underneath it. You could extend the activity by asking the children to make up their own sentence using one or more of the target words.

Binoculars may be easier to use than a telescope.   The bicentenary of the Battle of Waterloo is on 18th June 2015.
I used to have a tricycle but now I have a bicycle.   The tetrahedron has triangular faces.

Look and write

binoculars

biceps

bicentenary

monorail

unicycle

monosyllable

bicycle

triangle

triangular

tricycle

Listen and write

_____ may be easier to use than a _____.

The _____ of the Battle of _____ is on 18th June 2015.

I used to have a _____ but now I have a _____.

The _____ has _____ faces.

Look, listen and learn

music	musical
musician	electric
electrical	electrician
machine	mechanic
mechanical	mechanism

Teacher's notes

Sheet A, Look, listen and learn: Use the words on this page as a focus for discussing phonic patterns and word structures. Encourage the pupils to observe the relationships between the base words and their derivatives – the words derived from 'machine' are particularly interesting. The words related to music have already been met in a previous list but provide clues for the other words in this list. Ask pairs or small groups of children to create two spoken sentences using some of the words.

Sheet B, Look and write: Encourage the children to look closely at the words and to practise writing them.

Sheet B, Listen and write: Dictate each sentence below to the children, emphasising the target words and the revision words. The word complicated can be segmented very effectively. Encourage the children to copy each sentence in full on the line underneath it. You could extend the activity by asking the children to make up their own sentence using one or more of the target words.

The electrician played music while he worked.   The electrical wiring in a house can be very complicated.
The machine played two musical notes then stopped working.   The mechanic decided that there was a fault in the mechanism.
The musician played an electric guitar.

Look and write

music	musical
musician	electric
electrical	electrician
machine	mechanic
mechanical	mechanism

Listen and write

The _____ played _____ while he worked.

The _____ wiring in a house can be very _____.

The _____ played two _____ notes then stopped working.

The _____ decided that there was a fault in the _____.

The _____ played an _____ guitar.

Look, listen and learn

wonder	wonderful
beauty	beautiful
colour	colourful
peace	peaceful
skill	skilful

Teacher's notes

Sheet A, Look, listen and learn: Use the words on this page as a focus for discussing phonic patterns and word structures. Can the children observe the patterns in extending the base words to add suffixes? Ask pairs or small groups of children to create two spoken sentences using some of the words.

Sheet B, Look and write: Encourage the children to look closely at the words and to practise writing them.

Sheet B, Listen and write: Dictate each sentence below to the children, emphasising the target words and the revision words. Encourage the children to copy each sentence in full on the line underneath it. You could extend the activity by asking the children to make up their own sentence using one or more of the target words.

I wonder which is the most beautiful flower.   The Northern Lights have wonderful colours.
The man was wearing a very colourful tie.   Behaviour in the playground should always be peaceful.
The musician was very skilful when he played the piano.

Look and write

wonder	wonderful
beauty	beautiful
colour	colourful
peace	peaceful
skill	skilful

Listen and write

I _____ which is the most _____ flower.

_____

The Northern Lights have _____ _____.

_____

The man was _____ a very _____ tie.

_____

Behaviour in the _____ should always be _____.

_____

The _____ was very _____ when he played the

_____.

_____

Look, listen and learn

swim	swam
swimming	swimmer
trim	trimmed
trimming	trimmer
slip	slippers

Teacher's notes

Sheet A, Look, listen and learn: Use the words on this page as a focus for discussing phonic patterns and word structures. Can the children observe the patterns in extending the base words to add suffixes? Do they notice the odd one out? Ask pairs or small groups of children to create two spoken sentences using some of the words.

Sheet B, Look and write: Encourage the children to look closely at the words and to practise writing them.

Sheet B, Listen and write: Dictate each sentence below to the children, emphasising the target words. Introduce the word 'favourite', pointing out its structure before dictating the sentences. Encourage the children to copy each sentence in full on the line underneath it. You could extend the activity by asking the children to make up their own sentence using one or more of the target words.

The swimmer swam three lengths in her fluffy slippers!   My favourite sport is swimming.
I had to trim the paper but I trimmed too much off.   The hedge needs trimming when it stops raining.

Look and write

swim	swam
swimming	swimmer
trim	trimmed
trimming	trimmer
slip	slippers

Listen and write

The _____ _____ three lengths in her fluffy _____!

_____

My _____ sport is _____.

_____

I had to _____ the paper but I _____ too much off.

_____

The _____ needs _____ when it stops _____.

_____

Look, listen and learn

city	cinema
centre	celebrate
celebration	celebrity
December	cereals
certificate	circus

Teacher's notes

Sheet A, Look, listen and learn: Use the words on this page as a focus for discussing phonic patterns and word structures. As with Set 11, ask the children to compare the sound made by each letter 'c' – do they notice that sometimes the letter 'c' represents the phoneme /k/ and sometimes the phoneme /s/? In the words 'certificate' and 'circus' the first 'c' represents /s/ and the second represents /k/. Ask pairs or small groups of children to create two spoken sentences using some of the words.

Sheet B, Look and write: Encourage the children to look closely at the words and to practise writing them.

Sheet B, Listen and write: Dictate each sentence below to the children, emphasising the target words and the revision words. Encourage the children to copy each sentence in full on the line underneath it. You could extend the activity by asking the children to make up their own sentence using one or more of the target words.

I went to the cinema in the centre of the city.   Lots of people celebrate in December.
I like to have cereal for breakfast.   The celebrity attended the celebration when the new film came out.
I have lots of certificates for swimming.

    Andrew Brodie: Improving Spelling for Ages 9–10 © A&C Black, Bloomsbury Publishing 2011

Look and write

city	cinema
centre	celebrate
celebration	celebrity
December	cereals
certificate	circus

Listen and write

I went to the _____ in the _____ of the _____.

Lots of _____ _____ in _____.

I like to have _____ for _____.

The _____ attended the _____ when the new film came out.

I have lots of _____ for _____.

Look, listen and learn

camera	catalogue
courage	encourage
encouragement	cover
recover	discover
discovery	recovery

Name   Date

Look and write

| camera | catalogue |

| courage | encourage |

| encouragement | cover |

| recover | discover |

| discovery | recovery |

Listen and write

I looked in a _____ to find the best _____.

_____

The teacher _____ the boy to show _____ in the

football _____.

_____

_____

The tennis player needed lots of _____ to win the _____.

_____

The _____ had to _____ the ball from the _____!

_____

Once the doctor _____ what was wrong, the girl made a quick

_____.

_____

_____

Look, listen and learn

fright	frighten
frightening	flight
height	delight
delighted	midnight
tonight	headlight

Teacher's notes

Sheet A, Look, listen and learn: Use the words on this page as a focus for discussing phonic patterns and word structures. Can the pupils identify what all of the words have in common? Can they observe how some of the base words have been extended with prefixes or suffixes? Ask pairs or small groups of children to create two spoken sentences using some of the words.

Sheet B, Look and write: Encourage the children to look closely at the words and to practise writing them.

Sheet B, Listen and write: Dictate each sentence below to the children, emphasising the target words and the revision words. Encourage the children to copy each sentence in full on the line underneath it. You could extend the activity by asking the children to make up their own sentence using one or more of the target words.

My mum gets very frightened by thunder and lightning.   The Wright brothers' first flight did not reach a great height. She was not delighted when she had to leave the ball by midnight.   The electrician uses a headlight when he works. It would be a delight to see an owl tonight.

Look and write

| fright | frighten |

| frightening | flight |

| height | delight |

| delighted | midnight |

| tonight | headlight |

Listen and write

My mum gets very _____ by thunder and _____ .

The Wright brothers' first _____ did not reach a great _____ .

She was not _____ when she had to leave the ball by

_____ .

The _____ uses a _____ when he works.

It would be a _____ to see an owl _____ .

Andrew Brodie: Improving Spelling for Ages 9–10 © A&C Black, Bloomsbury Publishing 2011

Look, listen and learn

niece	piece
field	thief
chief	leaf
beneath	each
friend	wheat

Teacher's notes

Sheet A, Look, listen and learn: Use the words on this page as a focus for discussing phonic patterns and word structures. Do the children realise that most of the words feature the phoneme /ee/, with two different graphemic representations? Can they identify the odd one out? Ask pairs or small groups of children to create two spoken sentences using some of the words.

Sheet B, Look and write: Encourage the children to look closely at the words and to practise writing them.

Sheet B, Listen and write: Dictate each sentence below to the children, emphasising the target words and the revision words. Encourage the children to copy each sentence in full on the line underneath it. You could extend the activity by asking the children to make up their own sentence using one or more of the target words.

My niece was eating a big piece of cake.   The thief hid in the field but the police found him.
The chief of the bank has a very large car.   The frog was sheltering beneath a very large leaf.
My friend likes cereal made from wheat.

Andrew Brodie: Improving Spelling for Ages 9–10 © A&C Black, Bloomsbury Publishing 2011

Name

Date

Look and write

niece

piece

field

thief

chief

leaf

beneath

each

friend

wheat

Listen and write

My _____ was eating a big _____ of cake.

_____

The _____ hid in the _____ but the _____ found him.

_____

The _____ of the bank has a very large car.

_____

The frog was sheltering _____ a very large _____ .

_____

My _____ likes _____ made from _____ .

_____

Look, listen and learn

collect

collector

collection

reflect

reflector

reflection

reflective

construct

constructor

construction

Sheet A, Look, listen and learn: Use the words on this page as a focus for discussing phonic patterns and word structures. Do the pupils notice that all of the words feature 'ct'? Can they think of other words related to 'collect', 'reflect' or 'construct'? Ask pairs or small groups of children to create two spoken sentences using some of the words.

Sheet B, Look and write: Encourage the children to look closely at the words and to practise writing them.

Sheet B, Listen and write: Dictate each sentence below to the children, emphasising the target words and the revision words. Encourage the children to copy each sentence in full on the line underneath it. You could extend the activity by asking the children to make up their own sentence using one or more of the target words.

The stamp collector had a collection of over five thousand different stamps.
I saw the reflector on listhe bicycle when the car lights shone on it.   The still water showed a perfect reflection of the boat.
I tried to construct the highest tower possible using my construction bricks.

Look and write

collect

collector

collection

reflect

reflector

reflection

reflective

construct

constructor

construction

Listen and write

The stamp _____ had a _____ of over five

_____ different stamps.

I saw the _____ on the _____ when the car lights

_____ on it.

The still water showed a _____ _____ of the boat.

I tried to _____ the highest tower _____ using my

_____ bricks.

Look, listen and learn

confess	confession
possess	possession
impress	impression
professor	profession
processor	procession

Teacher's notes

Sheet A, Look, listen and learn: Use the words on this page as a focus for discussing phonic patterns and word structures. Do the pupils notice that all of the words feature double 's'? Can they think of other words related to 'confess', 'possess', 'impress', 'profess' or 'process'? Ask pairs or small groups of children to create two spoken sentences using some of the words.

Sheet B, Look and write: Encourage the children to look closely at the words and to practise writing them.

Sheet B, Listen and write: Dictate each sentence below to the children, emphasising the target words and the revision words. Encourage the children to copy each sentence in full on the line underneath it. You could extend the activity by asking the children to make up their own sentence using one or more of the target words.

I had to confess that I had eaten too many chocolates.   My friend also made a confession: that she had eaten too many crisps!
I wish I possessed a good memory so that I could make a good impression by remembering people's names.
The professor was able to impress everybody with his knowledge.
My computer has the latest processor so it's really fast.

Look and write

confess	confession
possess	possession
impress	impression
professor	profession
processor	procession

Listen and write

I had to _____ that I had eaten too many _____.

My _____ also made a _____: that she had eaten too many crisps!

I wish I _____ a good memory so that I could make a good _____ by _____ people's names.

The _____ was able to _____ everybody with his _____ .

My _____ has the latest _____ so it's really fast.

Look, listen and learn

heavy	heaviness
heavily	heavier
light	lightness
lightly	lighter
strong	strength

Teacher's notes

Sheet A, Look, listen and learn: Use the words on this page as a focus for discussing phonic patterns and word structures. Talk about what the words have in common, both in terms of meaning and of letter structure. For example, contrast how the suffix 'ly' is added to the words 'light' and 'heavy'. Ask pairs or small groups of children to create two spoken sentences using some of the words.

Sheet B, Look and write: Encourage the children to look closely at the words and to practise writing them.

Sheet B, Listen and write: Dictate each sentence below to the children, emphasising the target words and the revision words. Discuss the word 'gymnast' before dictating the sentences, pointing out the grapheme 'g' representing /j/ and the grapheme 'y' representing /i/. Encourage the children to copy each sentence in full on the line underneath it. You could extend the activity by asking the children to make up their own sentence using one or more of the target words.

My bag is very heavy when I carry it to school but it's a bit lighter when I go home.
The heaviness of the bag slows me down but I'm strong!
I trod too heavily in the mud so my shoes got very dirty.
The boy pressed so lightly with his pencil that it was difficult to see his writing at all.
The gymnast showed her strength in the floor exercise.

Look and write

heavy	heaviness
heavily	heavier
light	lightness
lightly	lighter
strong	strength

Listen and write

My bag is very _____ when I carry it to school but it's a bit

_____ when I go home.

_____

_____

The _____ of the bag slows me down but I'm _____!

_____

I trod too _____ in the mud so my shoes got very _____.

_____

The boy pressed so _____ with his pencil that it was _____

to see his _____ at all.

_____

_____

The _____ showed her _____ in the _____ exercise.

_____

Look, listen and learn

reply	replied
answer	answered
asked	called
speak	spoke
whisper	whispered

Teacher's notes

Sheet A, Look, listen and learn: Use the words on this page as a focus for discussing phonic patterns and word structures. All of these words could be used when pupils are writing conversations. Discuss the unusual past tense of speak. Ask pairs or small groups of children to create two spoken sentences using some of the words.

Sheet B, Look and write: Encourage the children to look closely at the words and to practise writing them.

Sheet B, Listen and write: Dictate each sentence below to the children, emphasising the target words. Encourage the children to copy each sentence in full on the line underneath it. You could extend the activity by asking the children to make up their own sentence using one or more of the target words.

I called my friend on the phone but there was no reply.   I tried again later and her mum answered.
Her mum spoke to me for ages, then I asked to speak to my friend.
"Who's speaking?" asked my friend, speaking only in a whisper.   "It's me!" I whispered in reply.

    Andrew Brodie: Improving Spelling for Ages 9–10 © A&C Black, Bloomsbury Publishing 2011

Look and write

reply	replied
answer	answered
asked	called
speak	spoke
whisper	whispered

Listen and write

I _____ my friend on the phone but there was no _____.

I _____ again later and her mum _____.

Her mum _____ to me for ages, then I _____ to

_____ to my friend.

"Who's _____?" _____ my friend, _____ only

in a _____.

"It's me!" I _____ in _____.

Look, listen and learn

possible	possibly
possibility	impossible
impossibility	probable
probably	probability
improbable	terrible

Look and write

possible	possibly
possibility	impossible
impossibility	probable
probably	probability
improbable	terrible

Listen and write

"It's _____ _____ to get all the work done by lunchtime," said the teacher.

_____

"Is there any _____ of you doing my work for me?" said my _____ lazy friend!

_____

"No, that would be _____," I _____.

_____

"What's the _____ of both of you finishing the work?" _____ the teacher.

_____

_____

"I think it's quite _____!" my friend _____ to me.

_____

Look, listen and learn

patient	impatient
patiently	impatiently
perfect	imperfect
important	importantly
immediate	immediately

Teacher's notes

Sheet A, Look, listen and learn: Use the words on this page as a focus for discussing phonic patterns and word structures. Can the pupils add suffixes to the word 'perfect'? Ask pairs or small groups of children to create two spoken sentences using some of the words.

Sheet B, Look and write: Encourage the children to look closely at the words and to practise writing them.

Sheet B, Listen and write: Dictate each sentence below to the children, emphasising the target words and the revision words. Encourage the children to copy each sentence in full on the line underneath it. You could extend the activity by asking the children to make up their own sentence using one or more of the target words.

The doctor's first patient was waiting patiently in the waiting room.   Some of the other patients were getting impatient. Another patient came in needing immediate attention.   "It's important that I help this patient immediately," said the doctor. "This may be the perfect time to make a new appointment!" said the first patient.

Look and write

patient	impatient
patiently	impatiently
perfect	imperfect
important	importantly
immediate	immediately

Listen and write

The doctor's first _____ was waiting _____ in the waiting room.

_____

_____

Some of the other _____ were getting _____.

_____

Another _____ came in needing _____ attention.

_____

"It's _____ that I help this _____ _____," said the doctor.

_____

"This may be the _____ time to make a new _____!" said the first _____.

_____

_____

Look, listen and learn

regular	regularly
irregular	response
responsive	responsible
irresponsible	responsibility
relevant	irrelevant

Teacher's notes

Sheet A, Look, listen and learn: Use the words on this page as a focus for discussing phonic patterns and word structures. Do the pupils notice that some of the words feature prefixes, some feature suffixes and that some of the base words are shown? Can they add extra suffixes, such as 'ly' to 'responsive' or 'relevant'? Ask pairs or small groups of children to create two spoken sentences using some of the words.

Sheet B, Look and write: Encourage the children to look closely at the words and to practise writing them.

Sheet B, Listen and write: Dictate each sentence below to the children, emphasising the target words and the revision words. Encourage the children to copy each sentence in full on the line underneath it. You could extend the activity by asking the children to make up their own sentence using one or more of the target words.

The tennis player practised regularly.   "Who was responsible for this accident?" asked the teacher.
"It's quite a good story but some of the sentences are not relevant," the teacher remarked.
"It's my responsibility to tidy up," said the bossy girl.   "Would you like a regular sized drink?" asked the barista.

Name

Date

Look and write

regular

regularly

irregular

response

responsive

responsible

irresponsible

responsibility

relevant

irrelevant

Listen and write

The tennis player _____ _____ .

_____

"Who was _____ for this _____?" _____
the teacher.

_____

"It's quite a good story but some of the sentences are not _____,"
the teacher _____ .

_____

_____

"It's my _____ to tidy up," said the _____ girl.

_____

"Would you like a _____ sized drink?" _____ the barista.

_____

Look, listen and learn

logic	logical
illogical	illuminate
illustrate	illustration
illustrator	imagine
imagination	imaginative

Look and write

logic	logical
illogical	illuminate
illustrate	illustration
illustrator	imagine
imagination	imaginative

Listen and write

Most maths _____ can be solved by thinking _____.

I like to _____ my stories with _____ pictures.

It takes a lot of lights to _____ a football _____.

The _____ used a lot of _____ when _____ the nursery rhyme.

The _____ book had lots of _____.

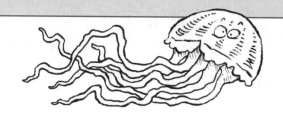

Assessment 1

My mum says it's cheating to use a **calculator** for **mathematics** but I don't think it is. Sometimes **calculations** such as **addition** and **subtraction** are easy to do without a **calculator** but **multiplication** and **division** are often very difficult. I think **fractions** and **decimals** are quite easy but **percentages** are a lot harder. It's a good idea to make an **estimate** or **approximation** before **calculating** the **answers** to maths **questions**.

I don't think you need to **calculate** so much when doing maths work about **shapes**. Mum says I need to know which ones have four sides. That's easy: **square**, **rectangle**, **rhombus** and **parallelogram**. I also know that a **triangle** has three sides and that a **circle** has only one side with no corners and that the middle of it is called the **centre**.

Write about one of your school subjects.

Assessment 2

Next year my **birthday** is on the second **Wednesday** of **February**. I would really like a **piano** but I think they're too **expensive** so I'll **probably** get a **recorder** instead! I suppose any sort of **musical instrument** will be fine as at least I will be able to learn **music**.

This year I got a mobile **telephone** with a built in MP3 player and **camera**. I was so excited, I didn't know **whether** to make a call, **listen** to **music** or take a **photograph**! I sat on the **sofa** and started to read the **instructions** but then the phone rang and I wasn't even sure how to **answer** it! I had a **wonderful** day.

Write about your own birthday.

Assessment 3

As they got closer to the **airport**, the family got more and more **excited**. They could see **aeroplanes** landing and taking off and **wondered** where each one was coming from or going to.

When they **arrived** they had to park the car then **travel** on a little **railway** to reach the main part of the **airport**. They still had to take another form of **transport** to reach the correct **terminal**: the **monorail**.

Josh was hoping that they would see a **celebrity** but Mum explained that the **celebrities probably travelled** first class so would be in a different part of the building. Josh was **disappointed** because he was hoping to get the **autograph** of somebody famous.

His **disappointment** didn't last long as he knew that the **flight** would be a **wonderful** experience.

What could happen next in this story?

Teacher's notes

The three assessment texts on the following pages can be used to sample pupils' progress, giving a 'snapshot' of their current level of competence in spelling. Most of the words appear in the sets of words that the pupils have been practising but others are introduced as they follow similar patterns to known words or follow phonic rules. Do the pupils use skills in syllabification and segmentation effectively?

Assessment 1 features 25 mathematical vocabulary words to spell. Multiplying each pupil's score by 4 will give a percentage result. Assessments 2 and 3 both have 20 words to spell and therefore multiplying by 5 will give their percentages.

To administer each test, dictate the full passage before issuing the test sheets. Dictate the passage again very slowly, ensuring that each child is keeping up with your reading. Allow time for the children to write each of the missing words.

You could use the assessments on several occasions to identify any progress, using only one test on each occasion. Are there particular words or spelling patterns that cause difficulties for some children? If so, would the pupils benefit from revisiting the lists that feature these?

As an extra activity you could ask the pupils to extend each story. What happens next? How well can the children spell the words that they choose for their own part of the story?

Assessment 1

My mum says it's cheating to use a _____ for _____ but I don't think it is. Sometimes _____ such as _____ and _____ are easy to do without a _____ but _____ and _____ are often very difficult. I think _____ and _____ are quite easy but _____ are a lot harder. It's a good idea to make an _____ or _____ before _____ the _____ to maths _____ .

I don't think you need to _____ so much when doing maths work about _____ . Mum says I need to know which ones have four sides. That's easy: _____ , _____ , _____ and _____ . I also know that a _____ has three sides and that a _____ has only one side with no corners and that the middle of it is called the _____ .

Score   /25 =   %

Assessment 2

Next year my _____ is on the second _____ of _____ . I would really like a _____ but I think they're too _____ so I'll _____ get a _____ instead! I suppose any sort of _____   _____ will be fine as at least I will be able to learn _____ .

This year I got a mobile _____ with a built in MP3 player and _____ . I was so excited, I didn't know _____ to make a call, _____ to _____ or take a _____ ! I sat on the _____ and started to read the _____ but then the phone rang and I wasn't even sure how to _____ it! I had a _____ day.

Score   /20 =   %

Assessment 3

Name

Date

As they got closer to the _____, the family got more and more

_____. They could see _____ landing and taking off and

_____ where each one was coming from or going to.

When they _____ they had to park the car then _____ on a

little _____ to reach the main part of the _____. They still

had to take another form of _____ to reach the correct _____:

the _____.

Josh was hoping that they would see a _____ but Mum explained

that the _____ _____ _____ first class so

would be in a different part of the building. Josh was _____

because he was hoping to get the _____ of somebody famous.

His _____ didn't last long as he knew that the _____

would be a _____ experience.

Score   /20 =   %

Andrew Brodie: Improving Spelling for Ages 9–10 © A&C Black, Bloomsbury Publishing 2011